Dear Friend...
Do You Know
About Tongue Ties?

written by
Dr. Catherine Murphy

illustrated by
Ira Baykovska

Dear Friend...Do You Know About Tongue Ties?

ISBN: 979-8-9865862-4-3
Library of Congress Control Number: 2022921706

Names, characters, and places are products of the author's imagination.
Front cover image, illustrations, and book design by Ira Baykovska.
First printing edition 2022.

Published by Rodney K Press
rodneykpress.com

Dear friend,

I created the character Pat as a collage of my patients. However, as I was wrapping up the edits, I realized that I drew much of the emotional aspect from my own childhood.

It took 30+ years to relate my ailments together. As I matured, the symptoms persisted and new ones were added, such as anxiety and irritable bowel syndrome (IBS). So I'm here to support you as one that endured this as a child, an adult, and as a mother of two tongue tied children.

This book is also dedicated to my amazing children, Patrick and Matilyn, and my husband, Mat. Thank you for transforming my life.

Motherhood fills my heart with joy while reminding me there are new lessons to learn every day. I'm not a perfect mom...however, each day I give you all that I can. Some days I'm all momma, some days I'm more at work, and sometimes I need more me time, but all days I show up with love, light, and laughter. As Nana says, "I love you the whole outside full."

May you learn that life is meant to be lived in harmony, not balance.

From the experts
in the field of tongue ties and tethered oral tissues

"Dr. Catherine Murphy has crafted a beautifully illustrated book to convey the effects of tongue tie and open mouth breathing on the health and development of children. Tongue tie occurs when the tongue is attached too tightly to the floor of the mouth and while it is common, it is still overlooked. From the early days of childhood development, tongue tie impacts on nursing and ability to breathe through the nose, as well as the formation of the teeth, jaws and airway. This has a knock on effect on sleep quality, mood and academic performance. As parents, we all want our children to reach their full potential. Addressing tongue tie and the habit of mouth breathing are necessary parts of this journey. This little book carries a big, important message and I am sure you will enjoy the read."

- Patrick McKeown author of *The Breathing Cure*

"Combining her own powerful maternal instinct with several years of professional training and clinical experience in the practice of Orthodontics, Catherine Murphy clearly, and rather poetically by the way, teaches her readers about the newly emerged scientific discipline of Pediatric Sleep-Breathing Hygiene. This important book is not only filled with delightful musical rhymes about serious health-related concepts, but is also beautifully illustrated by artist Ira Baykovska, which makes the story fun to read aloud and also fun to listen to. Over the 30+ years of my career as an academic and clinically practicing Pediatric Dentist, I have had the opportunity to review several wonderful stories intended to help educate parents and their kids about important health and wellness topics; this particular little volume rates very highly amongst the best of them. Enjoy learning!"

- Dr. Kevin L. Boyd, DDS, MSc(Nutrition and Dietetics)

"As a myofunctional therapist I love how this book introduces what to expect around a tongue-tie release. As a mom, I'm grateful for the way it prepares and encourages the child. Dr. Murphy has such a gift for teaching through her books while offering the most caring support through her words! Thank you again for another great one!"

- Renata Nehme, RDH, BSDH, COM®

"This book helps to make the complexity of tethered oral tissues easy to understand. As a recovering oral breather who didn't have her tongue tie released until almost 4 decades of life I would give anything for a book like this when I was a child. The compensations from a functional tongue tie affect the entire body and reduce one's quality of life in so many ways. This book is an amazing tool to help children thrive the way they where intended to."

- Ronda Holman, Dental Assistant aka The Airway Champion

"Dear Friend... is a precious and delightful resource to introduce the principles of tongue tie, tongue tone, and tongue space to the children who will become the adults of tomorrow. From myofunctional therapy, orthodontic treatment, to tongue-tie release, I am so impressed by how efficient and sweet the book is in terms of empathizing with children and at the same empowering them to take charge of their oral and whole body health and well-being."

- Dr. Soroush Zaghi, MD (ENT/Otolaryngology- Sleep Surgery)

"Dear Friend... Do you know about tongue ties? is an amazing little tale to help create those "ahaa" moments for parents and children surrounding tongue ties and overall health. Catherine has an amazing ability to create a relatable story and character, as this little guy's journey is unfortunately not unique to him. Thank you Catherine, for creating this beautiful resource that will increase airway health awareness and assist parents to connect the dots & find the right professionals to support their child."

- Myo Munchee CEO, Dr Mary Bourke, BAppSc, BSc.

"An adorable little book to help our little ones and their parents appreciate the impact of a functional approach to healthcare! Inspiring, sweet, beautiful, and fun. A must-have in the waiting rooms of every functional pediatric dental office. I would highly recommend this book for young children and parents alike!"

- Dr. Nora Zaghi, DDS

"As a specialized head and neck physical therapist and myofunctional therapist who treats tongue-tie pre and post releases, I realize the amount of stress this issue can cause for both child and parent. Having had two children who were tongue tied, I feel that this book is a wonderful resource for both mom and child. Addressing tongue-ties as quickly as possible and supporting the child with education and knowledge is the key to success. Thank you Dr. Murphy for this great contribution."

-Dr. Jenny Hobson, PT, DPT, MTC, CFC

"As a SLP, Feeding Specialist, Certified Myofunctional Therapist, Educator, and Podcaster in this space, it's exciting to see this information become more mainstream. Dr. Catherine Murphy highlights, once again, important topics that can change the trajectory of a child's health and their future for the better. As a mama who is on this journey with both of my children, thank you for another great resource to help spread the word on the impact of tongue tie and highlighting the positive impact of early intervention!"

Hallie Bulkin, MA, CCC-SLP, CMT, COM, QOM

These experts are incredible and trusted resources for you and your family.
Please search and learn from them on your preferred search engine and/or social media platform.

Wanna know a secret? I have a tongue tie story.

Mom didn't know at first, but soon found out,
no need to worry!

Ahh, life is so much easier now!

I was a messy eater, more food on my mouth than in!
As mom looked at me quizzically, I gave a messy grin.

When I was three, my family
noticed a peculiar sound.

I'd grind my teeth while fast asleep, my habit they had found.

Mom always carried lipbalm
since my lips
were cracked and dry.

The doctors blamed it
on prescriptions when
we asked them why.

My family said my teeth were weak so I wasn't allowed that many sweets.

They didn't know about hidden sugars or why they caused cavities and boogers.

My siblings wouldn't share a room with me
because I'd snore.

Mom said, "You're just like Grandpa
with your rumbling, resting roar."

I loved foods that got really soft
like crackers often do.
Mom tried to feed me carrots,
but they were so hard to chew!

The day that we switched dentists
I remember mommy cried.

The doctor talked forever.
We found out
I was tongue tied.

My tongue looked too big for my mouth.
We learned my jaws were small.

My dentist said that she could fix it for me after all!

I needed an appliance, I was nervous as could be.

But mom and I were ready. My tongue would now be free!

I learned to stretch and lift my tongue,
a practice new to me.

Mom said it was called "myofunctional therapy".

Goals of "myo"

1. Breathe through your nose, not your mouth

2. Lips together at rest

3. Proper tongue posture

4. Correct swallowing pattern

My jaw began to spread,
and my tongue had space to move!
One more quick procedure.

I was brave and I improved!

Mom and I were proud of all the work that we had done.

We celebrated with a treat and had a lot of fun.

We're grateful that we
know the root
of all these issues now.

My breath, my sleep
and how I eat — it's all
connected — wow!

Now I shared my secret – this is where my story ends.
I'd love to hear your journey.
Will you share it with me, friends?

Observation sheet

There are many symptoms to look for regarding your child's health that your healthcare providers often don't get to see. Additionally, many of these symptoms you may not have known were connected to your child's teeth or wellness. By observing these habits, you can get a better handle on the problem and watch for improvement.

Please check off what you observe. If you're not sure, check it anyway. Share with your provider.

While sitting around *(playing video games, doing homework, in the car, etc.)* does your child:

o   have trouble sitting still
o   put "things" in the mouth a lot (toys, sleeves, pencils, fingernails, etc.)
o   lick or suck on the lips
o   have the lips apart
o   stick the tongue out of the mouth
o   have the tongue resting between the teeth
o   lean the cheek on a hand
o   breathe with the mouth even slightly open
o   have noisy breathing

During snack time or a meal, does your child:

o   chew food with lips open
o   eat sloppily
o   stick the tongue between the teeth when swallowing
o   stick the tongue out to meet the drinking glass
o   make noises when chewing (smacks)
o   gasp for air while eating
o   take a breath before drinking
o   make the lips purse when swallowing
o   make the chin crinkle when swallowing
o   bob the head when swallowing
o   gulp liquids

While sleeping, does your child:

o   sleep walk and/or sleep talk

o   have nightmares, terrors

o   wet the bed

o   sweat

o   snore

o   appear to have difficulty breathing

o   ever stop breathing for a short time

o   gasp for air

o   have loud breathing

o   have the mouth open, even just a little

o   grind teeth

o   drool on the pillow

o   have restless sleep/toss and turn

o   tilt the head back

o   sleep on the stomach

o   wake up with dry throat or thirsty

o   wake up with chapped lips

o   have trouble waking up in the morning

o   wake up with dark circles under the eyes

o   wake up with headaches

In public or at school, does your child:

o   appear sleepy or actually fall asleep

o   crave sugary snacks

o   have trouble concentrating

o   exhibit hyperactivity

While talking, does your child:

o   talk too fast

o   talk too slowly

o   shift the jaw to the side

o   gasp for air

o   have a lisp

o   have a speech struggle

For further information, type
**"The Role of Dentistry
in the Treatment
of Sleep Related Breathing
Disorders"**
in your search engine.

About the Author

Dr Catherine (Cathy) Murphy aka The Holistic Orthodontist™ is a mom on a mission to transform health care from short term solutions to life enhancing treatments. From an early age, holistic options intrigued Cathy. She still has the first book she purchased on alternative therapies which included face massage, craniosacral therapy and more. The birth of her son and his dismissed mouth breathing caused her to commit to transforming her approach to orthodontics and dentistry. Viewing and treating crooked teeth as a symptom of an underlying cause has enhanced her patients' smiles and overall health.

Dr. Murphy is an orthodontist in the cozy suburbs of Chicago, IL. Her many years of advanced education enforced her appreciation in the beauty of a bicuspid. Viewing the mouth as the mirror of one's overall health is the fuel to her passion for dentistry and healthcare.

www.DrCatherineMurphy.com
Photo credit: Christina Irvin

About the Illustrator

Ira Baykovska is a children's book illustrator and a mom of two beautiful girls. Ira has been drawing for as long as she can remember and sometimes cannot believe that this hobby has become her life-long career.

She has been working as a freelance illustrator since 2014 and has illustrated more than 20 books for kids. Ira has a degree in Graphic Design and currently lives and works in Lviv, Ukraine.

www.baykovska.com
Photo credit: Galyna Ludchak

66778212R00024